The TROPICAL BLOSSOMS of the Bahamas, the Caribbean, the West Indies and the tropical part of South America have been photographed in their natural color and in their natural settings, and published for the pleasure of both the traveler and the residents of these areas. No attempt was made to photograph "perfect specimens" . . . their natural beauty was captured as it was seen . . . on the bush, plant or tree.

The flowers are arranged alphabetically by their most common names in the first part of the book. The flowering trees follow in alphabetical order in the second half of the book. The common names vary from one part of the Caribbean to the other, so the name found to be most generally in use was selected for purposes of alphabetizing. Reference to specific locations was accurate at time of publication.

Library of Congress Catalog Card Number: 60-15513

TROPICAL BLOSSOMS

Text and Color Photography

by

Dorothy and Bob Hargreaves

Published by

HARGREAVES INDUSTRIAL

P. O. BOX 4095 · PORTLAND 8, OREGON

Price $2.00 in U. S. funds, postpaid anywhere in the world from the publisher · Hard bound edition $3.50 postpaid

Also available at bookstores

AIR PLANT

Eng. Air Plant, Floppers, Cathedral Bells
Sp.   Prodigiosa, Flor de Aire

Bryophyllum pinnatum (Lam) Kurz

Grown-ups and children alike derive much pleasure from this balloon like plant. The children love to pop the funny little pinkish-green cylinders that grow on a tall spike from the center of the plant, and grown-ups, as well as children, enjoy picking a leaf and pinning it on a curtain. The leaves, true to their name, grow on air. Soon tiny roots will appear in each little scallop of the thick shiny leaves, and then an entirely separate plant develops. Bryophyllum means sprouting leaf. Cut flowers last well and make interesting arrangements. It can be grown indoors on air as well as soil on the mainland. (Also a Kalanchoe.)

Another plant that has the ability to thrive on air as well as soil is the bright red *Bromelia humilis* pictured above. The Bromeliads can often be seen perched on branches of trees and telephone wires. They are a relative to the pineapple as is the Spanish Moss one sees hanging from trees in the tropics. Fairchild Gardens, Florida; Botanical Gardens in Trinidad, Jamaica, and Tobago.

2

ALLAMANDA

ENG. Yellow Allamanda, Golden Trumpet, Yellow Bell, Buttercup Flower

SP. Alamanda, Canarias

Allamanda cathartica var. hendersonii (Bull) RAFFILL

This golden velvety flower grows on sprawling vines or shrubs. The tube spreads into five thick lobes with two or three buds opening at a time. They are pointed, brownish in color and look as if they had been varnished. The leaves are smooth, thick and pointed. It is of the Periwinkle family from Brazil, and often used as a cathartic. Will grow from cuttings. There is also a purple variety.

ALOCASIA

ENG. Giant Alocasia
SP.   Alocasia

Alocasia macrorrhiza SCHOTT

Very large heart-shaped leaves from four to five feet high shelter strange flowers up to a foot long. They have rather an unpleasant odor. Their milky juice is said to relieve pain from nettle stings. The plant can be seen in Fairchild Gardens in Florida, in Haiti and Caracas, Venezuela.

In Hawaii it is called an Ape (pronounced Ah-pay).

AMARYLLIS

Eng. Amaryllis, Barbados Lily
Sp. Tararaco, Azucena de Méjico

Hippeastrum equestre

This lily of many colors is from a bulb, from which it rises one to two feet high with lovely, showy flower trumpets. It usually blooms in the spring. The blossoms stay fresh several days, and are good cut flowers. Can be raised as a houseplant. Originally from South America.

SPIDER LILY

Eng. Crinum Lily, Milk-and-Wine Lily, Spider Lily
Sp. Lirio de cinta

Crinum zeylanicum

Crinum derives its name from "krinon," the Greek word for lily. It is a liliaceous plant of the Amaryllis family with six thin spidery petals and six stamens. The large leaves are two to six feet long and grow in a large clump from which springs the stem bearing its head of from five to thirty fragrant flowers. These may be pure white, striped, or tinted rose-purple. From tropical America.

ANTHURIUM

ENG. Anthurium, Flamingo Flower

Sp. Anturio

Anthurium andraeanum LINDEN

Like a mysterious unreal beauty, this waxen valentine truly typifies the tropical exotics. It is a beautiful member of the Arum family. (The Calla Lily is also a member of this family.) It ranges in color from pure white, pink-red, deep red, orange, red and green and many others. The flower is really a heart-shaped bract called the spathe. It is thick and leathery and looks artificial. From this six to nine inch spathe rises the spadix, white, pinkish, or yellow. The true flowers are on this spadix and are hardly noticeable. The leaves, too, are large, lovely, and heart shaped. One sees mostly the pink variety throughout the West Indies. These tropical American Exotics are very popular because of their beauty and their long lasting quality, which is three weeks if cut in their prime.

BEAUMONTIA

ENG. Beaumontia Vine, Herald's Trumpet,
    Easter Lily Vine

Sp.   Beaumontia

Beaumontia grandiflora (Roxb.) WALL

Big white blooms with a pinkish-brown cast to the out-side petals mark this delicately fragranted vine as one to be favored. It is a member of the Dogbane family from India. The flower is about six inches across with five lobes, but has a narrower and longer trumpet than the *B. jerdoniana* Wight pictured above. Fairchild Gardens in Florida.

BIRD OF PARADISE

ENG. Bird of Paradise, Queens Bird of
    Paradise Flower
Sp.   Estrelitzia, Ave de Paraíso

Strelitzia reginae BANKS

The exotic coloring and looks of this flower is undoubtedly known to many. The tall stalks look like the neck of a bird topped by a lovely head with a long beak and crest. This beak is a pointed sheath, greyish-blue in color. The crest of the bird is made up of flowers lifting out of the sheath; usually about six to a sheath. One pushes out each day or so, thus the cluster becomes larger and more colorful as it becomes older. The flower has three pointed petals, brilliant orange with blue staminodiums shaped like arrowheads. The flower stalks grow slightly above the clump of stiff paddle-shaped leaves which are about three or four feet long with a reddish vein down the center. They are a relative of the banana and a native of South Africa. Bloom intermittently, and will grow and bloom indoors. Fairchild Gardens in Florida.

WHITE BIRD OF PARADISE

Strelitzia nicolai THUNBERG

Curious flowers that grow on a small tree that looks like a palm. They have banana-like leaves, and look much like their relative, the Orange and Blue Bird, above. The sheath is purplish-blue-grey color, and is frequently smeared with a gummy substance as pictured.

BOUGAINVILLEA

Is named for a French navigator Louis A. de Bougainville.

ENG. Bougainvillea, Paper Flower
Sp. Buganvilea, Flor de Papel, Trinitaria

CRIMSON LAKE BOUGAINVILLEA

Bougainvillea glabra, var. Sanderiana choisy

These are long, colorful sprays of bright crimson flowers which are grown on the close cousin of the purple species (Spectabilis) pictured right. The leaves are small and triangular with wavy margins. The stems have thorns. They bloom profusely all through the Caribbean and South especially during the dry season. Native of Brazil.

CEREUS

ENG. Nightblooming Cereus, Cinderella Plant, Belle of the Night

SP. Flor de cáliz

Hylocereus undatus (Haw.) BRITT. and ROSE

Huge buds open about eight in the evening and last until about ten the next day never to open again. The Cereus only remains open until the sun and heat of the day wilts it. Then it droops and closes—a lovely flower presented to the world for a fleeting glimpse. It is a climber with fleshy, three-sided stems, scalloped and spiny. It pushes up walls, banks, trees and so forth for lengths up to sixty feet. One can watch the sepals and petals unfold to a beautiful bloom filled with many pale yellow stamens. The style is among these stamens like an individual flower (see the *Selenicereus grandiflorus* (L.) Britt. and Rose. Pictured above). This is from Jamaica and Cuba. There is another similar rare cactus from Trinidad and Tobago that has even larger flowers. The Cereus is called Cinderella Plant in Antigua because of the fleeting appearance it makes.

CHENILLE PLANT

Eng. Chenille Plant, Red-hot Cat Tail, Monkey Tail, Pussy Tail

Sp. Califa, Rabo de Gato, Roa de Mono

Acalypha hispida Burmann

This strange looking tropical shrub from the East Indies where it is used medicinally has long velvety tails of dark red up to eighteen inches long which resemble chenille. These tails are made up of staminate flowers without petals. They have dark green veined, rather pointed leaves. The young leaves of some are cooked and eaten. Member of the Spurge family, is seen throughout the West Indies and Puerto Rico.

11

CONGEA

ENG. Congea, Shower of Orchids Vine
SP. Lluvia de Orquideas

Congea tomentosa

These mauve-pink velvety ramblers that spill over in a lovely starlike shower are really the bracts practically hiding the tiny white flowers in the center. These bracts are long lasting and make graceful flower arrangements. The vine is a native of Burma related to the Petrea which it resembles (see Page 31). One sees it growing throughout the Caribbean, South America, Florida, Bermuda and the Bahamas.

CUP OF GOLD

ENG. Cup of Gold, Chalice Vine, Golden Chalice, Gold Cup

SP. Mendieta, Copa de Oro

Solandra nitida Zucc.

A spectacular flower with blossoms up to nine inches long. It blooms for four days, changing in color from light cream when in bud, to a golden banana color when in full bloom, to an orangish-apricot before it dies. (Smells a little like ripe apricots too.) The huge, waxy buds unfold almost before your eyes. It is a member of the potato family, and a native of Mexico and Tropical America. It can be a sixty foot jungle climber. The silver cup (*Solandra grandiflora* Sw.) from the West Indies differs mainly in having a whitish, funnel-shaped trumpet about ten inches long.

13

GINGER

Eng. Red Ginger, Ostrich Plume Ginger
Sp. Alpinia

Alpinia purpurata
(Viellard) SCHUMANN

The long, pretty waxen red bracts of these showy flowers look like the bloom, but the true flower is the small whitish bloom which appears from behind these bracts in the picture above. It is good for flower arrangements. Native of Malaya, it blooms most of the year.

Eng. Torch Lily, Torch Ginger
Sp. Lirio Antorcha *Phaeomeria magnifica*
(Roscoe) SCHUMANN

The fifteen foot bamboo-like stalks with large, bright green leaf blades, not unlike a small forest, practically conceal the spectacular torch bloom that springs up like an independent plant three to six feet tall beside the leaf stalks. These are one of the showy heads of the world! Native of Netherland East Indies. Others in red or wine come from Asia, and a lovely pink variety is grown in Haiti at the Chatelet des Fleurs.

Eng. Shell Flower, Shell Ginger
Sp. Colonia

Alpinia nutans (Andres) ROSCOE,
syn. *A. speciosa* (Wedl.) K. Schum.)

The shell-like flowers which spill out of the top of the twelve foot stalks have an almost porcelain texture. They are white, tipped in delicate pink. Prolific bloomers, they are native of tropical East Asia where they are used to make rope and paper, Puerto Rico, St. Croix and other Virgin Islands, Antigua.

HELICONIA

Eng. Heliconia (derived from Mt. Helicon in Greece)
Sp. Barco de Caridad, Plátano Cimarrón

Heliconia elongata R. F. Griggs

This unreal looking exotic has a pinkish sheath edged with yellow and green. The large bracts make spectacular and long lasting flower arrangements.

15

HELICONIA—Hanging Heliconia

Heliconia collinsiana GRIGGS

These bracts are similar to the Lobster Claw (see next page). They, too, have bright red keels, but they jut out of the stem and, instead of going up straight, as the Lobster Claw, they hang gracefully toward the ground. They have striking bright yellow flowers inside the keel. The Heliconia grows wild in Tobago and Trinidad. Puerto Rico has a yellow variety, and Hope Gardens, Jamaica, has an orange and yellow variety. Smaller Heliconia often used in yard plantings. (See picture at left.)

HELICONIA—Lobster Claw

Heliconia humilis JACQUIN

This Heliconia grows in a clump of tall, paddle shaped leaves (Banana family). The real flowers are inconspicuous inside the sheaths that are so colorful. They are a native of Tropical America. The bracts are bright red and suggest the red of boiled lobster claws—excellent for flower arranging. The Heliconia (Balisier) is the emblem of the Government of Trinidad.

HIBISCUS

ENG. Hibiscus
SP. Hibisco, Mar Pacifico, Pabonas

Hibiscus is one of the outstanding flowers of the tropics. They are all sizes, shapes and colors. They are quite unique because they possess the trait of not wilting for an entire day after picking. If needed for decoration at night, buds should be cut early and kept in the refrigerator. Buds picked the night before will open fully the next morning. Whether on the shrub, or laid out for all to behold, Hibiscus remain fresh and beautiful until nightfall when they quietly close and fade—a lovely gift to the world for a brief span of a day.

CORAL HIBISCUS

ENG. Fringed Hibiscus, Fuchsia Hibiscus, Coral Hibiscus, Chinese Lantern
SP. Farolito Chino

Hibiscus schizopetalus HOOKER

The dainty little coral colored frilled Hibiscus with the slender and gracefully curving stem is the parent of many hybrids. The petals are small, pendulous, fringed and lacy.

HYBRID HIBISCUS

As crossing is easy, there are many, many species of Hybrid Hibiscus. The pollen of one flower dabbled on the pistil of another, after its pollen is removed, produces seeds in a month and will blossom in a year. Many new hybrids have been sent from Hawaii where the Hibiscus is the new 50th State Flower.

Hibiscus bloom almost continually throughout the year. They have five petals, five stigmas, five lobes to calyx. They usually grow upright, but when they gracefully curve, they are related to the Coral Hibiscus (see left page).

Throughout the world the Hibiscus furnishes beauty, food (Okra), medicine, perfume, dye.

TREE HIBISCUS

Eng. Mountain Mahoe, Cuban Bast
Sp. Majagua

Hibiscus elatus Sw. syn. *Paritium elatum*

This is a useful true Hibiscus of the West Indies. As the flower grows older during the day, it turns to bronze and then red before it drops at nightfall.

TURK'S CAP

Sleeping Hibiscus, Pepper Hibiscus

Malvaviscus arboreus CAVANILLES

This funny little flower is like a closed red Hibiscus. It looks like the red Shriner's or Turk's Fez.

HONOLULU ROSE

ENG. Honolulu Rose, Wood Rose (sometimes called the Ceylon Morning-glory and Spanish Arbor Vine)

SP. Rosa de Madera

Ipomoea tuberosa LINNAEUS

The Honolulu Wood Rose is a well known vine of strange and attractive appearance. It looks like a rose carved of wood and polished to a beautiful satiny-brown finish. Actually, it is the dried seed pod of a species of morning-glory. (See the yellow blooms in the picture.) The central bulb contains the seeds. This is surrounded by graceful dried petals (calyx). The yellow flowers fall and the calyx begins to develop, enlarging into large, pointed, cream colored buds. These dry and open, and in a few days, the "Wood Rose" is stiff and beautiful. Before they lose their luster, they should be cut for lasting dried arrangements. The vine is a perennial which grows from seed. The shoots spread rampantly during the summer months covering trees, buildings, fences and whole fields. Rose usually matures in February. It takes about three months from blossom to rose.

These are used extensively in Honolulu for dried flower arrangements.

IXORA

Eng. Ixora, Jungle Flame Ixora,
Flame of the Wood,
Jungle Geranium
Sp. Santa Rita, Ixora Guillermina,
Cruz de Malta

Ixora macrothyrsa Teijsmann
and Binnendijk

This is a member of the Coffee family from the East Indies. It blooms most all year, but summer and fall are its best seasons. The big, bright, round "snowball" heads of scarlet blossoms are very showy. The small individual flowers have four petals. These grouped together make a big round ball up to six inches across. The Ixora's leaves are glossy and handsome. The flowers and bark are used medicinally. Cut flowers last well and are effective in arrangements. There are many colors which are grown in hedges, shrubs, etc., in Puerto Rico, Virgin Islands, and throughout the West Indies, Venezuela, and Florida.

MADAGASCAR JASMINE

ENG. Madagascar Jasmine, Stephanotis
SP. Estefanote

Stephanotis floribunda BRONGNIART

The Madagascar Jasmine, or Stephanotis, is a lovely vine with thick leathery, opposite leaves. The flowers are the familiar wedding bouquet flower. They have waxy, white, fragrant, trumpet-shaped flowers, and are two inches long with five lobes. They hang in clusters of six or eight on the vine. Milkweed family from Madagascar. The cucumber-like fruit, when ripe, is full of thin, silky-winged seeds . . . notice seed pod in background.

MEXICAN CREEPER

Eng. Mexican Creeper, Coral Vine, Loves Chain, Corallita
Sp.   Coralillo, Rosa de Montana

Antigonon leptopus Hooker and Arnott

Found along the banks, in hedges, on fences, and clambering beside the road is this lacy, bright pink flower. A native of Latin America (Mexico) where it is called Cadena del Amor—Chain of Love.

The flowers suggest strings of small pink hearts. They have no petals. The flowers are calyx with five petal-like sepals. Leaves, too, are heart-shaped with wavy margins. They belong to the buckwheat family, and are beloved by the bees. Found throughout the Caribbean. Also white and light pink variety.

MUSSAENDA

ENG. Mussaenda, Ashanti Blood
SP. Mussaenda

Mussaenda erythrophylla SCHUM. and THONN.

The bright African shrub is another member of the Coffee family. It is a most striking sight with the small star-like creamy white five-petaled one and one-half inch flowers with a center of crimson hairs contrasted with their enlarged two and one-half inch lobe of the calyx of deep scarlet. There are also white and yellow varieties, and an orange variety from India. Fairchild Gardens, Florida and Hope Gardens, Jamaica.

OLEANDER

Eng. Oleander, Rose Bay
Sp. Adelfa, Rosa Francesa

Nerium oleander LINNAEUS

Since the introduction of the clear pink Oleander, it has grown quite popular in the West Indies, Florida, etc. It is of the Periwinkle family from Asia Minor. Shrubs grow up to twenty feet tall, but can be kept low and bushy by pruning each summer into hedges, shrubs, or background trees. The leaves are slender, pointed, and a dull green. The branches are tipped with clusters of flowers, some single with five petals, others double. The colors range from white through cream, pink rose, and red. The shrub is poisonous and food cooked on the wood can even poison.
Blooms continuously.

ORANGE TRUMPET VINE

ENG. Orange Trumpet Vine, Flame Vine

SP. Lluvia de Oro

Pyrostegia ignea (Vell) PRESL.

From January through April, this blazing vine is a most spectacular sight to behold. The flowers are long, slender tubes with four or five lobes which curl gently back. The leaves are bright green, pointed and glossy. It is a member of the Bignonia family from Brazil. Cypress Gardens and Fairchild Gardens in Florida, Panama, Brazil, Trinidad, and other islands in the area.

27

ORCHIDS

There are so many species of orchids (over 700) that a separate book could be written just on orchids.

There are many nurseries and private homes that grow orchids similar to the Vanda Hybrid and the Cattleya pictured. Fairchild Gardens in Florida, Botanical Gardens in Trinidad, Agricultural Experimental Station in Trinidad, Hope Royal Botanical Gardens of Jamaica.

PAGODA FLOWER

ENG. Pagoda Flower, Clerodendron, Glorybower

SP. Guardia Civil, Cógetelo Todo

Clerodendron speciosissimum VAN GEERT
syn. *C. squamatum* VAHL.

A rich blending of fuchsia tones distinguish this member of the Verbena family. They bloom in large, rather loose, upright heads. The individual flowers are five narrow lobes which turn back against the tube. The stamens and pistil curve beyond this flower in small red tufts. The star-shaped calyx may thicken and enclose the interesting, small, shiny, berrylike fruit. The leaves are large, heart shaped, thick and velvety with deep veins. The stems are downy. There is a bright red variety (*C. rojo*) which is popular in the West Indies, Puerto Rico, Florida, and the Virgin Islands.

29

PRICKLY PEAR

ENG. Prickly Pear, Indian Fig
SP. Tuna brava, higo de mar

Opuntia megacantha SALM-DYCH

The Pinelands of South Florida have thirty species of this cactus which grows to a height of fifteen feet. It has yellow or orange flowers up to three inches in diameter from which develop pear shaped edible fruits about three inches long. This grows throughout the Caribbean in arid areas. On the Dutch Island of Curacao it is called Juffrouw.

PETREA

ENG. Blue Petrea, Purple Wreath Vine, Lilac, Queens Wreath
SP. Petrea

Petrea volubilis JACQ.

There is also a small evergreen tree called *Petrea arborea* that is very much like the vine above. The vine and the tree both bear profuse sprays of lovely bluish-violet flowers which cascade from its branches. The sepals are lighter in color than the corolla and outlast them on the tree leaving it a dull grey color. These sepals are the wings for the seed. This is called Liane St. Jean in Haiti. It can also be found in Florida, Trinidad, Tobago, Venezuela, British Guiana, Antigua, Barbados, and many other places. There is also a white variety called (*P. kohautiana*) Bridal Wreath. (See picture at right. Note the Periwinkle *Vinca rosea*, in the background.)

31

POINSETTIA

ENG. Poinsettia
SP. Flor de Pascuas, flor de noche buena

Euphorbia pulcherrima WILLDENOW

The flower that is the symbol of Christmas belongs to the Spurge family from Mexico. The Pionsettias that bloom so beautifully are sometimes double with huge shaggy heads of many red leaves. The true flowers are in the center. (See tiny yellow flower in center of picture at the left.) They bloom for a long period of time as hedges, shrubs, and spectacular yard plantings. If untrimmed, they will grow to twelve feet or more, but they flower better if cut back once or twice a year. They bloom by the length of time they receive daylight. Thus are called a "short day" bloomer as they usually bloom when the days are shorter. Brilliant street lights have postponed blooming period. Also pink and cream colors.

33

SHRIMP PLANT

ENG. Shrimp Plant, Shrimp Bush
Sp. Cola de Camarón

Beloperone guttata BRANDEGEE

These rosy-brown bracts are heart shaped and overlap each other on a curving stem. This makes them suggest a scale that looks like the curved tail of the shrimp—thus the name. The true flowers are white and tubular with purplish veins on the lower lip of two lobes. Guttata means speckled. Acanthus family from Mexico. Hope Gardens, Jamaica; Botanical Gardens, Trinidad; Tobago; Fairchild Gardens, Florida; and throughout warm climates. Can be grown as a houseplant.

WHITE SHRIMP PLANT

Justica betonica

Green and white spikes of heart shaped bracts with green veins. True flower is lavender and white.

SPATHIPHYLLUM

ENG. Spathiphyllum
SP.   Espatifilo

Spathiphyllum patinii (Hogg) N.E.BR.

A blossom like a small, white Anthurium only more fragile looking. The leaves grow about two feet high and are long and pointed and blade-like in very rich dark green. They are used for low growing cover in shady tropical gardens. They do not last when cut, however. Member of the Arum family from tropical America. There are some good specimens in the greenhouse at Hope Gardens, Jamaica, Cypress Gardens, Florida.

THUNBERGIA

ENG. Thunbergia, Sky Flower, Bengal Clockvine, Bengal Trumpet
SP. Fausto

Thunbergia grandiflora

One of the loveliest blues in the tropical garden is the Thunbergia or Sky Flower. It will thrive practically anywhere, and it blooms almost continually. The funnel-shaped blue flowers of five lobes have a pale yellow throat. They are borne in hanging racemes. The blue is very effective when combined with the yellow Allamanda (see Page 3), or the white Thunbergia. A native of India of the Acanthus family. May be seen in Fairchild Gardens and on patios in Florida; Puerto Rico, Haiti, Jamaica, and many other places in the warm climates.

FLOWERING TREES

YELLOW POUI (Also see Pink Poui, Page 56) *Tabebuia serratifolia*

The Yellow Poui is one of the largest and strongest of tropical forest trees. A single cubic foot of one of the trees may weigh from 60 to 80 pounds. The Brazilian timber known as pao d'arco, and the Surinam greenhart from the Guianas comes from this beautiful tree. Because it is resistant to insects and decay, it is used for fence material in Venezuela; also bridges, railroad ties, docks, etc. Few trees can surpass it for durability. Some U. S. manufacturers use it for fishing rods, canes, and similar items. However, the *beauty* of the tree cannot be surpassed either. It brightens the day as does the sunshine. The leaves appear after the flowers fall. It is said that after the tree has flowered the rains can be expected. Called El Araguaney in Venezuela; it is their national blossom.

AFRICAN TULIP TREE

ENG. African Tulip Tree, Flame of the Forest, Fountain Tree, African Spathodea
Sp. Espatodea, Tulipán, Tulipán Africano, Caobo de Santo Domingo

Spathodea campanulata BEAUVOIS

Palisot Beauvois first found this tree on the Gold Coast in 1787. The natives call their tree of fire blossoms the Baton de Sorcier. They believe it is an agent of witchcraft and black magic. The fiery red flowers of this large tree of the Bignonia family grow in circular groups around closely crowded buds, developing a few at a time, thus insuring blooms the year around. The seed pods up to two feet long are boat shaped. The tree is called the Fountain Tree because the unopened buds, when pinched between the fingers, will spurt compressed water to the delight of small boys who use them as water pistols. Birds are often surprised upon receiving a spray if their beaks pierce a bud.

AMHERSTIA

ENG. Amherstia, Pride of Burma, Orchid Flower
Sp. Amherstia

Amherstia nobilis

"Queen of the flowering trees" is named after Lady Amherst, wife of a Governor of Burma. It is called Toha in its native Burma (also Java). It is considered one of the most beautiful of all flowering trees. In 1857 it was brought to the botanical gardens in Trinidad where one of the finest trees in the Western Tropics still grows in all its superb beauty (see picture). The lovely vermilion orchid-like sprays droop gracefully two or three feet below handsome foliage. Each flower 8 by 4 inches hangs down on a slender red two inch stem from the central stem. The three upper petals are like the the wings of a butterfly; one is white speckled with red fading into a bright golden spot. Each branch on the 50 foot tree, which flowers most of the year, may produce these long lovely racemes. Besides the trees in Trinidad Botanical Gardens and Experimental Station, there is one in Hope Gardens, Jamaica.

ANGEL'S TRUMPET TREE

ENG. Angel's Trumpet Tree, Daturas, Angel's Tears

Sp.   Campana

Datura candida (Pers.) PASQUALE

The large swaying trumpets on this small tree look as if they had been placed there to decorate a Christmas Tree. They are around ten inches long and have five thin segments each coming to a twisted point. In the evening, they give off an exotic scent of musk. The leaves are large, greyish-green, thick and velvety. The flowers and leaves are poisonous to eat, but the natives sometimes smoke them as an asthma remedy. The whole plant contains a strong narcotic. They bloom intermittently.

BOMBACACEAE

ENG. Bombax, Wool and Cotton Tree
SP. Lana, Palo de Lana (Fromagier—Haiti)

The Bombax family, often called "Shaving Brush Trees," include 150 species of trees from many tropical countries. The trunks of some are enlarged for water storage, some yield balsa wood, kapok, fiber, gum, edible fruit and medicine. Colors are pink, white, yellow and red.

The one pictured above, *Bombax ellipticum* HBK. has breathtaking pink plumes which spring out from a bare tree like Ostrich Plumes. The bud, growing upright, is like a stubby cigar rising from the calyx. It splits into five parts, peels back like one peels a banana, and curls. The lovely pink pompons jut out with huge pink stamens five inches long. This one is from Mexico, while another Bombax from India is called the Red Silk Cotton (*Bombax malabaricum* D. C.). In Burma the fleshy red calyces of the large red flowers are collected as they fall to the ground and are used as a curry vegetable. This tree is more prevalent in the Caribbean area as is the Wild Chestnut, Estrella (*Pachira insignis*), so called because of its seeds which are edible. In the swamps of Trinidad one often sees aerial roots on the trees.

BOTTLE-BRUSH TREE

ENG. Bottle-Brush Tree
SP. Calistemon

Callistemon lanceolatus DE CANDOLLE

Kallistos Stamon are two Greek words meaning beautiful thread—stamens. Such are the long cylindrical spikes of bright red flowers that make the Bottle-Brush blossom. Like a gay brush that is used to clean bottles, these many tufts of red stamens droop down gracefully similar to the weeping willow. The foliage is narrow, pointed and fine, and belongs to the Myrtle family from Australia. The fruits harden and when dry look like little grey buttons. It is said that these can be counted to determine the tree's age. This tree is a relative of the Paper Bark, Cajeput Tree (*Melaleuca leucadenra* L.) which is popular in Florida. It has many layers of peeling bark and cream colored blooms. Puerto Rico, Virgin Islands, West Indies and other islands.

BROWNEA

There are several species of Brownea. The *B. macrophylla* L. above from Colombia is spectacular because of its bright red stamens. The huge flower pops out of the limb of the small evergreen tree like a big, red pin cushion. The *Brownea grandiceps* Jacq. is a similar 30 or 40 foot tree called Rose of Venezuela, Mt. Rose, and Rosa de Monte, Palo de Cruz, Rosa de Cruz to the Spanish. It too has bright red flowers of six or more inches. Brownea came from Dr. Patrick Browne, a pioneer naturalist in Jamaica in the 18th century.

CANNONBALL TREE

Eng. Cannonball Tree, Carrion Tree

Sp. Bala de Cañón, Coco de Mono

Couroupita guianensis Aublet

A huge tree, similar to the Elm, with heavy bark, produces these unusual flowers and fruits. The branches push right out of the heavy bark, and have no connection with the foliage at the top of the tree. The blooms are about five inches across. In some ways they look like the wood rose. The blossoms are followed by heavy, hard-shelled cannonball-like fruits six to eight inches across. When these ripen they contain a pulp that has a very unpleasant odor. The natives use the shells for calabashes. Also called: In Brazil, abrico de macaco, castanha de macaco, cuia de macaco, cuirana; in Trinidad, moke, muco; French Guiana, arbre a bombes, boulet de canon; Surinam, boesi, kalabasi, zuela, Mamey hediondo, muco mucuratu, taparo de chuco; Panama, zapote de mono, granadillo, palo de paraiso. Fairchild Gardens boskelebas; Panama, zapote de mono, granadillo, palo de paraiso. Fairchild Gardens in Florida, and Botanical Gardens in Trinidad.

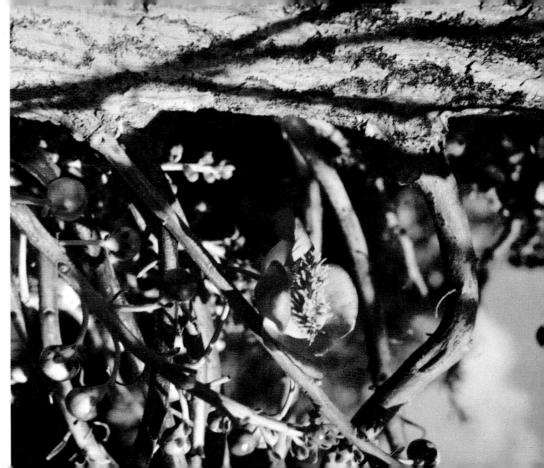

CASSIA

ENG. Cassia, Golden Shower Tree, Shower of Gold, Pudding Pipe Tree, Indian Laburnum, Purging Cassia

Sp. Cañafistola

Cassia fistula LINNAEUS

The shower trees belong to the Legume family. The Golden Shower has large clusters of bright yellow blossoms which tumble down, making the tree look as if it was always in the sunshine. The leaves are large and compound leaflets, two to six inches long. The flowers have five petals with a spike-like blossom. Long curving pistil and stamens project from the center of the flower. The pistil develops into the round black pod which grows up to three feet in length. This pod gives it the name of Pudding Pipe in India. A cathartic is made from its sticky brown pulp. The Indians also use the pulp added to their tobacco. Many trees in Jamaica, Trinidad, The Bahamas, Bermuda, and throughout the Caribbean.

PINK CASSIA

ENG. Pink Cassia, Pink and White Shower Tree,
Apple Blossom Cassia

SP. Cassia

Cassia javanica LINNAEUS

Another of the Legume family from Java. Its branches are completely surrounded by masses of unevenly tinted pink blossoms. Each petal is pale pink and white with deeper pink veinings, giving a variegated effect. The flower has five petals with a tuft of stamens from the center. They resemble apple blossoms and are often called the Apple Blossom Cassia. The tree is deciduous with the flowers preceding the leaves. The trees are not too large, but are quite irregular in form. Similar tree *Cassia nodosa* often seen in Puerto Rico and other tropical islands.

CORDIA

ENG. Cordia, Geiger Tree, Geranium Tree
Sp. Vomitel, Cutiperi

Cordia sebestena LINNAEUS

This is a small evergreen Tropical American tree indigenous to the Caribbean area and abundant from South Florida through the Bahamas and Jamaica where it is also known as an Anaconda or Spanish Cordia. It also grows wild in many of these areas. The tree likes dry conditions and thus flourishes in Antigua, Curacao (carawara Español), Aruba, Barbados (the large tree pictured here is from Barbados), and many other tropical islands from Puerto Rico (San Bartolemé) to South America. It is not cultivated as widely in Ceylon (Sebestens or Lolu) or Hawaii (Kou), but it was recently introduced into Zanzibar Africa, from Bermuda. Its bright orangish-red flowers form in many clusters of twelve to twenty flowers and buds. The blossoms begin to open first at the center of the cluster. The tubular flowers of about one inch across, are frilled and crepe-like.

FRANGIPANI

ENG. Frangipani, Pagoda Tree, Temple Tree, Plumeria
Sp. Franchipán, Lirio de la Costa, Alelí

Plumeria acuminata ATT. syn. *P. acutifolia* POIRET

There are many colors and varieties of Frangipani. One of the most common is the *P. acutifolia*, white with a larger yellow center than the one above, which is *P. obtusa* L. This lovely big white blossom is called the Singapore Plumeria, and it keeps its large dark-green Rhododendron-like leaves the year around, while the others shed theirs. The stem of all varieties exude a milky juice which will stain clothing. The French "frangipanier" (tree so called in French Guiana and Haiti) means coagulated milk, and by association was eventually used to refer to this tree. Plumeria was named after Charles Plumier, a French botanist who made voyages to the Caribbean in the seventeenth century. (It was originally spelled Plumieria.) Because of the wonderful sweetness of scent, the tree is often planted near temples and burying grounds in Ceylon, East and West Indies, Hawaii. Thus the name Temple Tree. The Hawaii Blossoms are used for leis to be hung around the visitor's neck. Trees can easily be started from cuttings. In Venezuela this tree is called amapola, atapaimo, tamaiba.

JACARANDA

ENG. Jacaranda, Fern Tree
SP. Framboyán Azul, Jacarandá

Jacaranda acutifolia HUMB. and BONPL.

One sees so many bright, warm colors in the tropics, that the cool, violet blue of the Jacaranda is rather startling. These grow to large trees with light grey bark covered with bi-pinnate foliage like a fern. In fact they are referred to as the "Fern Tree" in Jamaica and Trinidad. They belong to the Bignonia family from Brazil, but one may view many of these soft lavender-blue lovely ornamentals from Florida to South America. It also grows profusely in Mexico and Central America, and there are about fifty species in the Western Hemisphere. One, not as common, the *J. filicifolia*, is known as the "princess" of the family. It is named from two Latin words, *filix* (fern) and *folium* (leaf). The flowers of all species look like little blue bells that resemble a carpet under the tree when they fall. Some curative properties have been attributed to the Jacaranda. The Indians of Brazil where the tree is called caroba, use the leaves; in Panama, the bark is used for skin diseases. Here it is called palo de buba. The natives of Venezuela, where the tree is called guarupa, use it for medicine as do the natives of Colombia. It is called samarapa in Haiti, the sand trysil in British Guiana, but barbatimao in French Guiana.

LIGNUM VITAE

Eng. Lignum Vitae
Sp. Guayacán, palo santo

Guaiacum officinale L.

Lignum Vitae means "wood of life." It is the heaviest of all commercial woods, and will sink in water. It is irreplaceable in its use in shipbuilding. The tough resinous brownish-green heartwood is renowned for use in propeller shafts (also used for bowling balls, mortars and pestles [bowls], pulleys, mallet heads, bearings, etc.). The small evergreen is slow growing and makes a nice ornamental tree. It has been a source of medicine for centuries. Today, the resin is extracted for medicine, stain, etc. The large clusters of felty blue flowers are at the branch tips. The orange fruit, which is heart shaped, follows the flowers and is often seen on the tree at the same time as the flowers. The tree is indigenous to Tropical America and thrives in Jamaica (many line the road on way to Hope Gardens), Colombia and Venezuela. Some are to be seen in Trinidad, Tobago and Hispaniola.

LONG JOHN

Eng. Long John, Mulato Tree
Sp. Tachí, barrabas, palo María, volador, hormigo

Triplaris surinamensis

A tall tree which often grows up to one hundred feet or more, but is very slender and graceful—see tree in picture. Perhaps this is why it is called Long John. In Surinam it is called "drei tin" which reminds one that when it blooms the dry time of the year is near. Venezuela and Brazil call it "tachí" because that is the name of the ant that eats out the center of the tree.

The flowers on the tree are white when young, pink in their prime, and brown at maturity. Enlarged calyces that grow after the petals dry are really more ornamental than the flowers as they are bright red surrounded by a one half inch tube-like fruit. When these fall, they look like many small helicopters gyrating to earth. Can be seen in the Botanical Gardens in Jamaica, Trinidad, Surinam, French and British Guiana.

OCTOPUS TREE

ENG.   Octopus Tree, Queensland Umbrella Tree

Sp.   Cheflera   *Brassaiopsis actinophylla* ENDLICHER syn. *Schefflera actinophylla*

This is a member of the Panax family from Australia which has blooms that are peculiar, long, spreading arms suggesting the octopus. First they are greenish-yellow, then light pink, then deep red. Then dark purple fruits follow (like little dried berries); these harden and the whole arm falls. Also used as a house plant.

ORCHID TREE

ENG.   Orchid Tree, Ox or Bull Hoof, Butterfly Flower Tree

Sp.   Casco de buey, palo de orquideas, urape   *Bauhinia monandra* KURZ

The pretty little deciduous tree from Tropical America with pink orchid-like flowers splotched with wine-red is called Napoleon's Cock Hat in Antiqua, Trinidad, and other Caribbean Islands. There are a number of Bauhinia Trees; lavender with purple called Mountain Ebony (B. variegata); white (B. binata). Bauhinia is named after the Bauhins, two medical brothers devoted to botany rather than medicine.

PARKINSONIA

ENG. Parkinsonia, Jerusalem Thorn
SP. Palo Verde, Junco Marino, Espinillo

Parkinsonia aculeata

A lovely fern-like tree, which from a distance resembles the Australian Pine, grows along the roads in Haiti. Here it is called Madam Yass. Its bright yellow blossoms blend into the lacy looking foliage, presenting a graceful picture to the passerby. The small tree is named for the English Botanist, John Parkinson. Also found in Hope Gardens, Jamaica, Cuba.

DWARF POINCIANA

ENG. Dwarf Poinciana, Pride of Barbados
SP. Framboyán Francés, Guacamaya

Poinciana pulcherrima LINNAEUS
syn. *Caesalpinia pulcherrima* (L.) SWARTZ

Bright clusters of fiery red (also yellow variety) flowers grow on the tips of this small graceful tree or shrub. This is not a true Poinciana, but a close relative. It has five petals which are margined by yellow. There are long stamens and a pistil projecting from the center of each butterfly-like flower. It has lacy foliage with prickly branches. Blooms most of the year, and is a member of the Legume family. It is the sacred flower of Siva in India. Can be seen in Florida, Puerto Rico, Virgin Islands, Trinidad, Caracas, and of course Barbados. Also Haiti, Jamaica, and other tropical areas.

POINCIANA

Eng. Poinciana or Flamboyant, Royal Poinciana, Flame Tree
Sp. Framboyán, framboyán rojo, flamboyán, arbol de fuego

Delonix regia (Bojer) RAFINESQUE

One of the most strikingly beautiful trees in the world. It blooms in dense clusters which make a solid picture of color (see cover picture). They burst into these scarlet orange blossoms often on a tree more than forty feet high, and soon after the fern-like foliage appears. The orchid-like flowers have five petals, one of which is white or yellow. Long curved brown pods hang on the tree for months after the flowers and leaves have gone. In some Caribbean Islands and Puerto Rico, the dried pods have been collected for fuel. It is a member of the Legume family, and a native of Madagascar. It is one of the most popular roadside trees from Florida through the West Indies despite the fact that its sturdy root system constantly breaks up the sidewalks. Many also in the Bahamas, Bermuda, Venezuela, and the Virgin Islands. It grows wild in Australia.

PINK POUI TREE

ENG. Pink Poui, Trumpet Tree
Sp. Roble maguiligua, palo blanco,
roble blanco, roble de savana

Tabebuia pentaphylla HEMSLEY

The Pink Poui is the national tree of Salvador (called Maquilishuat). It is an outstanding yard tree as well as an excellent shade tree for coffee and cocao bushes (see page 61). The tree is of the Bignonia family averaging around sixty feet, but it will flower when only two years old. It resembles a great bouquet of pinkish-lavender petunia-like trumpets. The wood is used for commercial timber for the interior finishing of many ranch style houses. It is called Amapa in Mexico. Roble means oak.

POWDER PUFF TREE

Eng. Powder Puff Tree, Redhead
Calliandra, Mimosa

Sp.   Calliandra, Granolino

Calliandra inaequilatera Rusby

Calliandra is Greek for "beautiful stamens." Such is the Powder Puff Tree from Bolivia. Its long silky stamens form a lovely powder puff flower which looks as if it might have been dabbed in the rouge pot. It is a small tree or shrub (100 known species) from the warm parts of America, India, etc. One of the Mimosa family, its fern-like branches are dotted with the fluffy red pompons.

This is called Lehua Haole in Hawaii, where it is used to make an unusual feathery lei. (Also a white variety.) Another Lehua of Hawaii (Island of Hawaii's flower) is the native Ohia, *Metrosideros collina* (Forst.) Gray subsp. *polymorpha* (Gaud)—see picture above. On the slopes of Mauna Loa and Mauna Kea the trees reach 100 feet. They grow at altitudes from 1000 to 9000 feet. The blossoms are full of honey which is the food of the "iiwi," a bird with scarlet plumage that matches the blossom. The Hawaiians believe these red Lehua groves are sacred to Pele, the Goddess of Volcanoes. When angry, Pele destroys these groves with streams of lava. They say that if a Lehua is plucked on the way to the mountain, it will rain. The wood was used for idols and spears, but is now used for flooring, furniture, fuel and interior furnishing. Similar Calliandras in the Caribbean (Hope Gardens, Jamaica).

QUEEN OF FLOWERS

Eng. Queen of Flowers, Queen's Crepe Myrtle, Queen Flower, Queen Lager, June Rose, Pride of India

Sp. Reina de las flores, astromelia

Lagerstroemia speciosa (L.) Pers.

Another one of the most brilliant floral displays is a native of India where it is called "jarool." Used decoratively and as timber because it is tough and hardy for marine building (boats and fittings, canoes, ships, wharves, etc.) It is a favorite also in Asia, Australia, Philippine Islands, Africa, Central and South America, the Caribbean (particularly Jamaica and Trinidad), and South Florida. In June, when it is usually at its best, it is indeed a royal sight—Queen of the Flowers. Its rose-like blossoms vary from mauve to various shades of pink.

has six petals, and the oval fruit following the flower is also quite pretty. The tree is deciduous and grows up to fifty or more feet in India, but in other tropical regions averages only around twenty feet. The plant is often also called *L. regia, reginae, flos-reginae*. *Speciosa* comes from Latin *speciosus* meaning fair or pleasing to the eye. A similar smaller shrub, native of Tropical Asia, also grows in Florida and many of the above areas including Barbados and the Bahamas. It is called a Crepe Flower (*Lagerstroemia indica*).

TIGER'S CLAW

ENG. Tiger's Claw, Crabclaw Coral Tree, Indian Coral Tree
SP.   Piñón de costa, bucare

Erythrina indica LAMARCK
syn. *Erythrina variegata* var. *orientalis* (L.) MERR.

The large, spreading deciduous tree bursts into pointed red pea-shaped blossoms in midwinter and early spring. Flowers are a deep, rich red on the bare tree. Long spikes jut out of woody stems on the ends of the branches. The individual flowers break out of the split side of a pointed calyx with one flower petal much larger than the others, giving the effect of a pointed claw or feline toenail. The seed pods too, resemble pointed claws. Native of tropical Asia, member of the Legume family. There are about thirty species of Erythrina growing in the tropics. Erythrina is from the Greek word Erythros meaning red. In many regions these trees are known as "poison trees." The trees furnish toxic poison from the bark and seeds. The natives take this poison and stupefy fish so that they can easily catch them. The flowers, however, have never proved poisonous. The natives even use them for seasoning called "barbatusco" in Colombia, and in Guatemala the blossoms are used as a vegetable in soup and salads.

Two other Erythrina Trees found extensively in the Caribbean and Central and South America are the *E. poeppigiana* (Mountain Immortelle), brought to these areas 300 years ago for shade for coffee and cacao plantations (see Page 61). Also the *E. glauca* (Swamp Immortelle).

WILD COTTON TREE

Eng. Wild Cotton, Buttercup Tree, Yellowsilk, Shellseed
Sp. Palo bobo, potija

Cochlospermum vitifolium (Willd.) Spreng

From Tropical America these slender ornamental trees of about forty feet have clusters of golden flowers resembling giant buttercups. After the five, three to five inch poppy-like petals fade, the fruit capsule of about three inches forms containing a number of kidney-shaped seeds covered with long white floss, which is the "cotton" of the tree. This is often used like Kapok for stuffing pillows and mattresses. The tree is deciduous and usually blooms when leafless. The grapevine-like leaf of the tree gives it the Latin name viti (grape) folium (leaf). In Puerto Rico there is a double flowered petal variety which usually blooms in February and March. Called Carnestolendas in Venezuela (probably because it blooms during Lent) and njoe fodoe in Surinam. Known as tecoma suche in Central America and Mexico. Also called bototo and poro-poro.

CACAO

ENG. Cacao, cocoa
Sp. Caca-uatl, Trujillano

Theobroma cacao

Throughout Trinidad and Tobago (also other West Indies, Central American, and Mexican countries) one sees the large cacao pods hanging from their small evergreen bushes, but shaded by a large protective tree—see Poui (Page 56) and Erythrina (Page 59). Trinidad is one of the chief cacao producing countries of the world. It is cultivated for the seeds that are contained in these red pods. They are the source of cocoa, chocolate and cocoa butter.

SEA GRAPE

ENG. Sea Grape, Seaside Grape
Sp. Coccolola

Coccolola uvifera

The Sea Grape grows abundantly from Florida throughout the Caribbean, South America, and the Pacific Islands. It is an evergreen shrub or small tree with large, beautiful, kidney-shaped, leathery leaves and edible fruit that are violet when ripe. (Makes interesting arrangements.) As it is quite resistant to salt spray it is often seen along the beach. The yellowish-white blossoms are inconspicuous (see left of large cluster in picture).

61

AKEE

Eng. Akee
Sp. Akee   *Blighia sapida*, Ken.

This large, striking evergreen tree is named after the English Mariner, Captain Bligh of the "Bounty" and "Mutiny" fame. These bright red fruits follow a small white blossom. When the tree is covered with these three inch colorful fruits, it has a gay festive red and green Christmas-tree look. As soon as the three angled fruit "pops" open on its own, the aril that holds the shiny black seed is edible. But the fruit must be allowed to open naturally, for unripe ones are very poisonous. This is called the Akee in Jamaica, where it is very

popular sautéed and served with codfish. There are many of these trees in Jamaica. Also in Fairchild Gardens in Florida.

CASHEW NUT

Eng. Cashew
Sp. Marañón

Anacardium occidentale

A tall spreading tree that grows up to forty feet and thrives in dry open areas has tiny fragrant pink flowers (see center of picture) that produce an edible heart-shaped seed which is delicious when roasted—Cashew Nut. The orange upper part (see top of picture) is also edible, but the hulls have an oil used for linoleum and paints which will cause blistering if it gets on the skin during roasting.

62

BANANA

ENG. Banana (70 species)
SP. Banana, Guineos, Plátano
(cooking variety) *Musaceae*

Musa is used for roofs, cattle feed, clothing, medicine, dye, alcohol, wine, vinegar, etc. The fruits grow rapidly underneath each "ear" of the colored bracts. Each plant bears one bunch then is cut down and a new shoot around the base grows into another tree.

PASSION FLOWER

ENG. Passion Flower (400 species)
SP. Granadilla *Passifloraceae*

A highly ornamental blossom thought to be symbolic of the Crucifixion; the ten sepals and petals suggest the ten apostles; and darker circle, the halo or crown of thorns; the five stamens, the wound; the three styles the nails; the leaves, the hands of the persecutors. *P. edulis flavicarpa* Degener bears an edible fruit green in the picture below, but turns yellow when ripe. This is grown commercially for its fruit juice. (In Hawaii, called "Liliko'i).

CORDYLINE

Eng. Cordyline, Dracaena, Rayo,
Boundary Mark, Landmark,
Dragon's Blood

Sp. Pabola

Cordyline terminalis

Tones of red from dark maroon to bright pink appearing in irregular strips along the line of the veins mark the Cordyline pictured right. It is of the Liliaceae family and a native of the temperate and warm regions similar to the Dracaena (Greek for Dragon). In fact it is called a Dracaena in Trinidad and Jamaica. This family not only includes many ornamentals such as the Easter Lily, Tulip, Lily of the Valley, Yucca, but also many edible plants such as onions, chives, asparagus. It is used for medicine, fibre, perfume, varnish, drink (Okolehao in Hawaii). The Hawaiians use the green variety which they call Ti (pronounced tea) leaves for hula skirts. One can place a section of the woody stem in water and have an attractive house plant. In many places in the Caribbean it is used to mark boundaries.

Acknowledgment:

Flowering Trees of the Caribbean,
Introduction by WILLIAM C. WHITE

Flowering Plants from Cuban Gardens,
by the Garden Section of
The Woman's Club of Havana

In Gardens of Hawaii,
by MARIE C. NEAL

What Flowering Tree is That?
by EDWIN A. MENNINGER

Tropical Planting and Gardening,
by H. F. MACMILLAN

FRANK G. MACKANESS, *Horticulturist,*
Portland General Electric Co.

Fairchild Tropical Gardens,
Miami 56, Florida

Trinidad Botanical Gardens,
Trinidad

Gov. Agricultural Experimental Station,
Trinidad

Hope Royal Botanical Gardens,
Kingston, Jamaica

Hawaii Blossoms,
by DOROTHY and BOB HARGREAVES